DOUG the PUG®

DRESSED FOR SUCCESS

10 9 8 7 6 5 4 3 2 1   20 21 22 23 24
Printed in the U.S.A.   40

First printing 2020

Illustrated by Mercedes Padró
Written by Megan Faulkner
Photo Selection by Megan Faulkner
Book design by Jessica Meltzer

WHAT'S INSIDE?

ACM PARTY FOR
A CAUSE FESTIVAL

PEOPLE'S
CHOICE AWARDS

CMT MUSIC
AWARDS

LATIN GRAMMY
AWARDS

KID'S CHOICE AWARDS

SHORTY AWARDS

CMT MUSIC
AWARDS

CMT MUSIC
AWARDS

LAS VEGAS

INSIDE
DOUG'S
CLOSET

DOUG

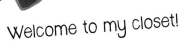

Welcome to my closet!

I'm known for my big *pug*sonality, but I'm even more famous for my *pug*mazing style! From red carpets and coffee runs to lazy days on the couch, I'm always dressed for success!

The style and fashion tips in this book will help you look and feel your very best!

— Doug

IN MY CLOSET THERE ARE:

5 ONESIES

ONE IS THE COZIEST NUMBER.

7 ROBES

NOT JUST
FOR BATH TIME
ANYMORE!

BYE, BYE BEDHEAD!

8 SHOWER CAPS

10 PLAID SHIRTS

IT'S A PLAID, PLAID WORLD.

14 BEANIES

BAD HAIR
DON'T CARE.

20 WIGS

EXPRESSING
MY PUGSONALITY
SINCE 2012.

DO

WEAR NATURE
ON UR HEAD

DON'T
WEAR NATURE ON UR FACE

19

DO

CELEBRATE UR
FAVORITE FOOD

DON'T

BECOME THE
MAIN COURSE

DO

BE COZY

DON'T
LIMIT YOURSELF

23

DO

WEAR WHAT U LIKE

DON'T
WORRY ABOUT THE HATERS

25

DO

LOVE YOURSELF—
WRINKLES AND ALL

DON'T
BE AFRAID TO SHOW THEM OFF!

WHAT SHOULD DOUG WEAR?

Being a style icon is hard work!

From red carpets and photo shoots to meet-and-greets with fans, I'm always looking for the perfect outfit. Will you be my stylist for the day and pick my outfits? On each page put a check mark beside your favorite look.

HELP!

☑ ROBE

IT'S A RED CARPET EVENT! WSDW?

IT'S JUICY COUTURE!

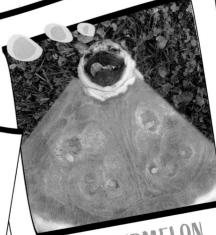

☐ WATERMELON DRESS

☑ CLASSIC TUX

WHEN U CAN'T WALK IN HEELS

☐ FANCY DRESS

COFFEE RUN! WSDW?

WHAT DO U MEAN "NO SHIRT, NO SERVICE?"

☑ BLANKIE

☐ SWEATS

☐ PLAID

ABERCROMBIE AND PUG

31

IT'S A BIRTHDAY PARTY! WSDW?

☐ HIS SUNDAE BEST

☐ DAD SHIRT

NO IRONING REQUIRED

☑ HIS BIRTHDAY SUIT

32

IT'S PUGOWEEN! WSDW?

☐ SOMETHING CUTE

☐ SOMETHING SCARY

☑ SOMETHING SILLY

GOT MY EYES ON U

33

IT'S THE FOURTH OF JULY! WSDW?

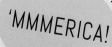
'MMMERICA!

☑ PATRIOTIC PARTY BLING

☐ SUNGLASSES AT NIGHT

☐ BBQ BOSS WEAR

34

IT'S CHRISTMAS! WSDW?

☐ CRUSTY T-SHIRT

☑ WHATEVER HE CAN FIND

☐ TUTU AND ANTLERS

I'M THE SUGAR PUG FAIRY!

#TRENDING

When it comes to sniffing out the latest trends, I'm always ahead of the pack. I've never met a trend I didn't want to try (especially the food ones). Check out my looks on the following pages and decide for yourself - is this trend IN, OUT, or CLASSIC?

HAWAIIAN SHIRT

☐ IN ☐ OUT ☑ CLASSIC

TEDDY BEAR COATS

☑ IN ☐ OUT ☐ CLASSIC

NON-TRADITIONAL HAIR COLOR

☐ IN ☑ OUT ☐ CLASSIC

STRIPES

☐ IN ☐ OUT ☑ CLASSIC

WHITE KICKS

☑ IN ☐ OUT ☐ CLASSIC

38

METALLICS

☑ IN ☐ OUT ☐ CLASSIC

DAD CHIC

☐ IN ☐ OUT ☑ CLASSIC

UNICORNS

☐ IN ☐ OUT ☑ CLASSIC

ANIMAL PRINTS

☐ IN ☐ OUT ☑ CLASSIC

39

DENIM JACKETS

☐ IN ☑ OUT ☐ CLASSIC

FLOWER CROWNS

☑ IN ☐ OUT ☐ CLASSIC

BAND T-SHIRTS

☐ IN ☐ OUT ☑ CLASSIC

JUMPSUITS

☐ IN ☐ OUT ☑ CLASSIC

PUFFER COATS

☐ IN ☑ OUT ☐ CLASSIC

SCRUNCHIES

☐ IN ☐ OUT ☑ CLASSIC

OVERALLS

☑ IN ☐ OUT ☐ CLASSIC

SKULLS

☑ IN ☐ OUT ☐ CLASSIC

FUZZY BOOTS

☑ IN ☐ OUT ☐ CLASSIC

LEATHER JACKETS

☐ IN ☐ OUT ☑ CLASSIC

AVOCADOES

☑ IN ☐ OUT ☐ CLASSIC

HIPSTER BEARDS

☐ IN ☑ OUT ☐ CLASSIC

42

NEON

☑ IN ☐ OUT ☐ CLASSIC

SPORTS JERSEYS

☑ IN ☐ OUT ☐ CLASSIC

ONESIES

☑ IN ☐ OUT ☐ CLASSIC

BEANIES

☐ IN ☐ OUT ☑ CLASSIC

43

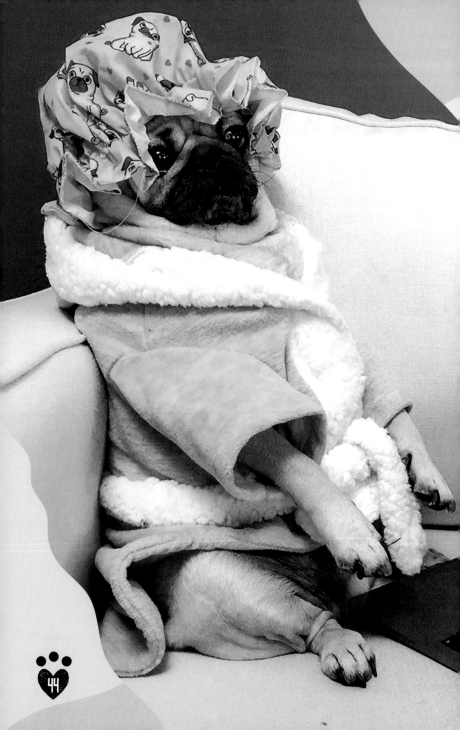

DEAR DOUG

FASHION EDITION!

Dear Reader,

Thank u for ur letters! I love hearing from fans. Here are my very best answers to ur most stylish questions.

- Doug

45

Dear Doug,

Which fashion faux paws do you secretly love?

—Breaking Rules in Brownsville

Dear Breaking Rules,

If socks and sandals are wrong, I
don't want to be right.

                    —Doug

Dear Doug,

What's the secret to looking comfortable and relaxed in photos?

–Uptight in Upland

Dear Doug,

What is your ugliest Christmas sweater?

-Curious in Culver City

Dear Curious,

There are no ugly Christmas sweaters.
Each one is beautiful.

-Doug

51

Dear Doug,

Do horizontal stripes really make you look wider?

—Wondering in Wyoming

Dear Wondering,

Nah. That's
a myth.

-Doug

53

Dear Doug,

What makes a great fall photo?

—Falling Flat in Falmouth

Dear Falling,

LEAVES + SHADES =
PERFECTION

—Doug

BONUS

MUG

PLAID

55

DOUG 🐾 TAILS

FILL-IN-THE-BLANK FUN!

THINGS TO KNOW:

NOUN: a person, animal, place, or thing.
Examples: teacher, fox, park, fork

ADJECTIVE: describes a person, animal, place, or thing. Examples: tall, furry, busy, smooth

VERB: an action. Examples: dance, walk, play

EXCLAMATION: a sudden cry or remark of surprise, anger, or pain. Examples: "Oh, my goodness!", "How could you?" or "Ouch!"

HOW TO PLAY: Ask a friend or family member to provide words for the blank spaces, but don't show them the pages, it's a surprise! Once you've filled in all the blanks, read the story out loud.

Example:

I can't wait to go to the ___**moon**___ ! I love
     place

___**snoring**___ in the ___**juicy**___ ___**dump truck**___ .
verb ending in "-ing"   adjective   noun

DOUG TAILS

MAKING IT BIG

Once upon a ___fox___ there lived a(n)
noun

___fork___ pug named ___Duge___. He/she
adjective   first name

dreamed of making it big. ___Duge___, ___singing___
same first name   verb ending in "-ing"

hard, dressing up as ___spiderma___, ___Billeish___,
superhero   popstar

___stink___, and ___Mack___ and posting
book character   movie character

photos and videos for fans. ___Duge___ survived
same first name

on ___pezza___ and ___coffe___, until
food   liquid

one morning he/she woke up to find he/she had ___20___
number

followers. "___yay___!" yelled ___Duge___,
exclamation   same first name

"I never have to eat ___pezza___ again!" "From
same food

now on it's ___Donuts___ and ___souroring___
different food   different liquid

for me!"

THE END

57

DOUG 🐾 TAILS

A DAY IN THE LIFE OF DOUG

My day begins at __7__ O' clock when my __clock__

starts __ringing__. After a __1__-hour bath,

I get dressed in my favorite __shirt__.

For breakfast, I put __eggs__, __Bacon__,

and __coffy__ in a blender to make a(n) __Breffkt__

smoothie. Next, I __sit__ on the couch and watch

__Hit me__ until my __legs__ starts

__vibrating__. I order a __chezz__

pizza with extra __chezz__. " __Yay__!"

I yell when it finally arrives. After lunch I take a

__2__-hour nap. Then it's time to get ready for a

night out. I put on my fanciest __sut__ and

head out the door. __Fingrs__ crossed - I'll get

to meet __Alex morgan__.

DOUG TAILS

HOW TO LIVE WITH A PUG

Pugs are a lot like _us_ (plural noun), they always
sleep (verb) when you want them to _walk_ (verb).
You can't tell a pug to "_put that_ (command)", because a
pug will always _yell_ (verb) instead. Your pug
will eat _15_ (number) pounds of _pezza_ (food) per
day and grow to the size of a _hipo_ (noun). You will
need to brush your pug _0_ (number) times daily with a
toth (noun) to keep its coat _hethy_ (adjective) and
gree (adjective). Pugs love to sleep in _blankits_ (plural noun)
so be sure to have one in every room. If your pug
seems _sad_ (adjective) and spends a lot of time
peting (verb ending in "-ing"), get a _nap_ (noun) to keep
him company. Your pug will thank you, and you will
live happily ever after.

QUIZ UNLEASH YOUR PUGSONAL STYLE

Before I was a jet-setting fashion icon, I was just a lil pup with big dreams. Finding ur style can take a long time, but this quiz will help make that road a little shorter.

- Doug

LOOK MA, NO ROLLS!

IN MY BIG BOY PANTS

1. PICK A SCHOOL OUTFIT.

ANSWER: JAYMee

A. JEANS 'N' TEE

B. PINK 'N' PRETTY

C. MOODY 'N' MYSTERIOUS

D. BRIGHT 'N' BRASH

2. PICK A BEACH OUTFIT.

ANSWER: _Deek Sharky_

A. COOL 'N' CLASSIC

B. BOLD 'N' BRIEF

C. SLEEK 'N' SHARKY

D. FUNNY 'N' SUNNY

3. PICK A FRIDAY NIGHT ACTIVITY OUTFIT.

ANSWER: D

A. COUCH 'N' CONTROLLER

B. POSING 'N' PICTURES

C. LAPTOP 'N' RELAX

D. PEOPLE 'N' PARTIES

4. PICK A COSTUME.

ANSWER: _____

A. BRAVE 'N' BRAWNY

B. PRETTY 'N' PRINCESSY

C. CREATIVE 'N' CLEVER

D. WACKY 'N' SNACKY

5. PICK A BLANKIE.

ANSWER: _____A_____

A. PLAID 'N' PLUSH

B. FURRY 'N' FABULOUS

C. DARK 'N' DRAMATIC

D. SOFT 'N' SPICY

6. PICK A VACATION.
ANSWER: _____A_____

A. MOUSY 'N' MAGICAL

B. REGAL 'N' ROYAL

C. HIGH-RISES 'N' HUSTLE

D. SAND 'N' SURF

7. PICK A T-SHIRT.

ANSWER: _____

A. PLAIN 'N' PREPPY

B. FUN 'N' FLORAL

C. CARING 'N' SHARING

D. BRIGHT 'N' BUSY

68

SCORING

MOSTLY A — ALL AMERICAN PUG 2

Calm, cool, and casual you're the pug next door.
Comfort is the name of the game. With a closet full
of jeans, tees, and sweats you've got the basics
covered, and you'll never go out of style!

MOSTLY B — DIVA PUG ○

Fancy and fun you're the prettiest pug in the pack,
and the world is your runway. You love trying new
trends and making them your own. You're a style
star on the rise and a legend-in-the-making!

MOSTLY C — INDEPENDENT PUG |

Thoughtful and one-of-a-kind you're no cookie-
cutter trend hound (mmm, cookies). You pick clothes
that show your interests, hobbies, and feelings. You
have an artistic spirit and are a true work of art!

MOSTLY D — PUG OF THE PARTY 4

Colorful and confident you light up every room you
enter. Your sense of humor shines through and
brightens everyone's day. Keep having fun with
fashion and sharing your pawsitive vibes!

YOU'RE INVITED

Time: <u>4:00 pm</u> **Date:** <u>Tomorrow</u>

Location: <u>My Place</u>

Attire: <u>Ur Coziest Robe</u>

PARTY
LIKE A PUG

Whether it's just you and your BFF, or the whole pack's coming over, here's how to throw a pugerrific party you'll never forget!

ON UR MARK, GET SET, EAT!

IS THAT MY BELLY GROWLING?

71

WHAT TO WEAR

BEFORE THE PARTY:

🐾 Stock up on shower caps so your friends can put them on when they arrive! You can find these at most dollar or wholesale stores.

SHARE THE DRESS CODE:

🐾 Bring your favorite onesie, jammies, blankie, and/or robe.

AND SLIPPERS TO KEEP UR PAWS WARM!

WHAT TO EAT

PIZZA, OBVIOUSLY

🐾 Set up a make-your-own pizza station.
   Make the dough or use your favorite
   frozen pizza as a base and add all of your
   favorite toppings!

🐾 OR order from your favorite place!

SNACKS

🐾 The cheesier, the better!

SWEET TREATS

🐾 Make-your-own sundae station.

🐾 Donuts!

WHAT TO DRINK

Anything you want — just serve
in mugs!

GAMES TO PLAY

HIDE-AND-GO-SNACK

You will need:

🐾 Packaged snacks

DID SOMEONE SAY "SNACK?"

How to Play:

Pick someone to be "it." The remaining players close their eyes and count down together from 30. Meanwhile, the player who is "it" hides one packaged snack. When the countdown is over, players search for the snack. Whoever finds the snack gets to keep it and becomes "it" for the next round.

PIN THE TAIL ON THE DOUG

You will need: 🐾 Scissors
🐾 Blindfold   🐾 Markers
🐾 Tape, putty, tacks, or push pins

Instructions:

1. Carefully cut out the Doug play board on page 81 and ask an adult to attach to a wall using the tape, putty, tacks, push pins, or whatever you prefer! HELPFUL HINT: For a sturdier picture, tape to card stock or poster board!

2. With adult supervision, carefully cut out Doug's tail and accessories on page 83. If you don't have enough for each player, draw your own accessories to pin to Doug! Attach tape, putty, or push pins to each piece and set to the side.

3. Blindfold the player who is "up." Spin them around several times, then hand them the play piece to "pin" on the Doug. The player whose pieces are closest to where they belong wins!

PUG, PUG, DOUG

How to Play:

Pick someone to be "it." The remaining players sit in a circle facing each other and close their eyes. Whoever is "it," walks around the outside of the circle and taps each player lightly on the head saying "pug" with each tap.

When the picker taps a player and says "Doug," the sitting player must jump up and race the picker in the opposite direction around the circle and back to the player's spot. Whoever sits down in the spot first keeps the spot and the other player becomes the picker.

DOUGO!

It's like Bingo, but better dressed!

For 2-6 players. Need more cards for more players? Make your own with your favorite Doug pics!

You will need: 🐾 Glue 🐾 Scissors

Instructions:

I. Carefully cut out pages 85-101.

2. Carefully cut out the photo tiles, cards, and chips.

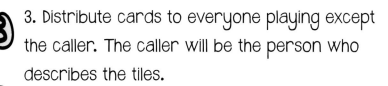

3. Distribute cards to everyone playing except the caller. The caller will be the person who describes the tiles.

4. The caller should mix the tiles face down in front of them.

5. The caller will pull one tile at a time and describe each image, showing it to each player
For example, "Doug in a red, plaid shirt in front of a bridge."

7. If the image is on your card, use a chip to cover your space. The first person with 5 chips in a row (horizontally, vertically, or diagonally) shouts "DOUGO" and wins the game.

HINT: Want to play alone? You can be the caller and player, just don't peek at the tiles!

THANKS FOR STOPPING BY!

I hope you had fun going through my closet with me and learning what it takes to dress for success!

Remember, I'm famous for my chill pugsonality. I don't recommend dressing pets in human clothes or feeding them human food. They may not be as laid back as I am.

C U Soon!

P.S. This isn't goodbye! Keep turning the pages to find the fun games I mentioned earlier, as well as a paper Doug to play dress-up with!

PUGTIVITIES!

That's right, there's still more fun! On the following pages find everything you need to play Pin the Tail on the Doug, DOUGO, and even a paper Doug on page 105 for you to dress!

ADULT SUPERVISION IS RECOMMENDED.

PIN THE TAIL ON THE DOUG GAME PLAY BOARD

Carefully cut out this page and hang it up to use as the play board for Pin the Tail on the Doug!

PIN THE TAIL ON THE DOUG TAIL & ACCESSORIES

Carefully cut out the tail and accessories to be used during Pin the Tail on the Doug!

DOUGO PHOTO TILES FOR CALLER

The caller will mix these tiles facedown in front of them, draw one at a time, describe the image, and then share it with each player.

Carefully cut along dotted lines.

DOUGO CARD FOR PLAYERS

Each player will use their card to look for the tile described by the caller. If a player has the image, use one chip to cover it.

Carefully cut along the dotted lines.

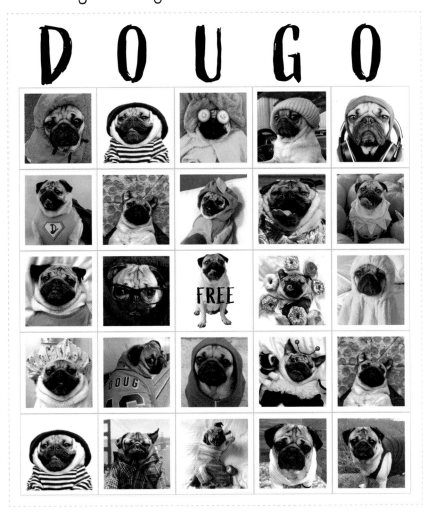

DOUGO CARD FOR PLAYERS

Each player will use their card to look for the tile described by the caller. If a player has the image, use one chip to cover it.

Carefully cut along the dotted lines.

DOUGO CARD FOR PLAYERS

Each player will use their card to look for the tile described by the caller. If a player has the image, use one chip to cover it.

Carefully cut along the dotted lines.

DOUGO CARD FOR PLAYERS

Each player will use their card to look for the tile described by the caller. If a player has the image, use one chip to cover it.

Carefully cut along the dotted lines.

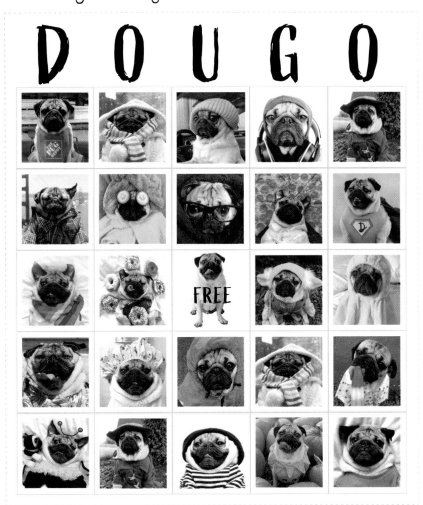

DOUGO CHIPS FOR PLAYERS

These will be used to cover the image the caller describes on your playing card.

Carefully cut along the dotted lines.

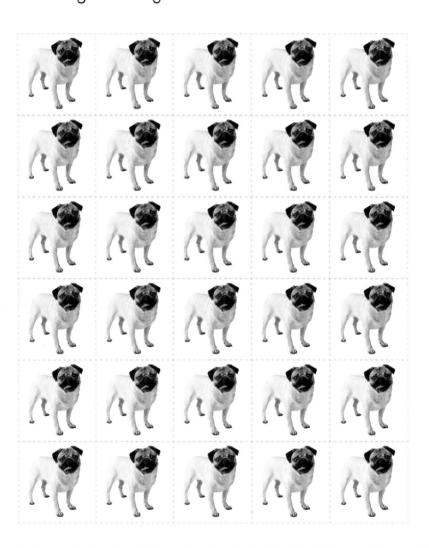

DOUGO CHIPS FOR PLAYERS

These will be used to cover the image the caller describes on your playing card.

Carefully cut along the dotted lines.

DOUGO CHIPS FOR PLAYERS

These will be used to cover the image the caller describes on your playing card.

Carefully cut along the dotted lines.

DOUGO CHIPS FOR PLAYERS

These will be used to cover the image the caller describes on your playing card.

Carefully cut along the dotted lines.

Do you ever feel like you just don't know what to wear?

Me, too! But with your help I know we can go from this...

To this!

TURN THE
PAGE TO
DRESS ME UP!

DRESS DOUG

Re-create Doug's most iconic looks! Cut out the following pages and glue them on to poster board or card stock. When dry, cut out Doug, the stand, and his pawesome wardrobe.

INSTRUCTIONS:

Cut Doug out along the dotted lines. To make Doug stand, fold the white part of the base back. Cut out the support along the lines. Fold at the foldline indicated to form a tab. Center the tab on Doug's back with the lower edge, even with the fold in the base. Tape or glue in place. For the accessories, carefully cut along the dotted lines and use the tabs to place accessories on Doug. Use tape to secure the tabs if needed. Ask an adult for help. Adult supervision is recommended.

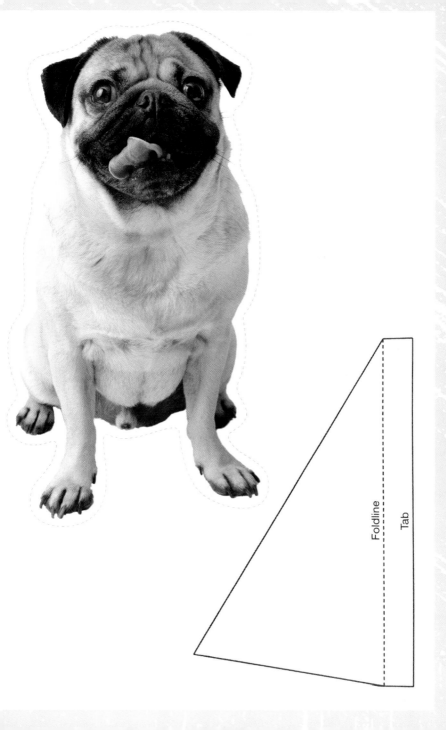

Foldline

Tab